ALONE AMID ALL THIS NOISE

A COLLECTION OF WOMEN'S POETRY

selected by **Ann Reit**

FOUR WINDS PRESS   NEW YORK

in memory of Mother

Published by Four Winds Press
A Division of Scholastic Magazines, Inc., New York, N.Y.
Copyright © 1976 by Scholastic Magazines, Inc.

Printed in the United States of America
Library of Congress Catalog Card Number: 75–38705

1 2 3 4 5   80 79 78 77 76

Library of Congress Cataloging in Publication Data
Main entry under title:

Alone amid all this noise.

1. Poetry—Women authors. I. Reit, Ann.
PN6109.9.A4   808.81   75–38705
ISBN 0–590–07359–1

Acknowledgments

For reprint permission, grateful acknowledgment is made to:

ANGUS & ROBERTSON (U.K.) LTD. for "Portrait" by Judith Wright.

MARÍA ARRILLAGA for "I Want for My Name" by Ángela María Dávila,
translated by María Arrillaga.

BARRIE & JENKINS LTD. for "She Warns Him" by Frances Cornford
from *Collected Poems*, published by The Cresset Press.

GEORGE BRAZILLER, INC. for "Vacant Possession" by Janet Frame from
The Pocket Mirror, copyright © 1967 by Janet Frame.

BROADSIDE PRESS for "personal letter no. 2" by Sonia Sanchez from
Home Coming, copyright © 1969 by Sonia Sanchez.

CORINTH BOOKS for "Mother Country" by Anne Waldman from
Giant Night, copyright © 1970 by Anne Waldman.

CROWN PUBLISHERS, INC. for "Kadia the Young Mother Speaks" by
Jessie Sampter from *A Treasury of Jewish Poetry*, edited by
Nathan and Maryan Auseibel, © 1957 by Nathan and Maryan
Auseibel.

A. GROVE DAY for "Warpath Song," "Wind Song," and "You May Go
on the Warpath" from *The Sky Clears*.

BABETTE DEUTSCH for "Moving" from *The Collected Poems of
Babette Deutsch* (Doubleday), copyright 1969 by Babette
Deutsch.

DOUBLEDAY & COMPANY, INC. for "The Blackbird" by Diane Wakoski
from *Inside the Blood Factory*, copyright © 1962, 1968 by
Diane Wakoski.

NORMA MILLAY ELLIS for "The courage that my mother had . . ." and
"Woman have loved before as I love now" by Edna St.
Vincent Millay from *Collected Poems* (Harper & Row),
copyright 1931, 1954, 1958 by Edna St. Vincent Millay and
Norma Millay Ellis.

FABER AND FABER LTD. for "The White Bird" by Anna Akhmatova from
Poems from the Russian, edited by Frances Cornford and
Esther Polianowsky Salaman.

Yiddish Poetry, edited by Irving Howe and Eliezer Greenberg, copyright © 1969 by Irving Howe and Eliezer Greenberg.

HOUGHTON MIFFLIN COMPANY for "Decade" by Amy Lowell from *The Complete Poetical Works of Amy Lowell*, copyright 1955 by Houghton Mifflin Company; "Her Kind" by Anne Sexton from *To Bedlam and Part Way Back*, copyright © 1960 by Anne Sexton; "Oysters" by Anne Sexton from *The Book of Folly*, copyright © 1972 by Anne Sexton.

OLWYN HUGHES, Literary Agent, for Canadian rights to "Childless Woman" by Sylvia Plath from *Winter Trees*, published by Faber and Faber, copyright 1971 by Ted Hughes.

JANE KATZ for "The Palm-Reading."

ALFRED A. KNOPF, INC. for "Let No Charitable Hope" and "Where, O, Where?" by Elinor Wylie from *Collected Poems of Elinor Wylie*, copyright 1932, 1928 by Alfred A. Knopf, Inc. and renewed 1960, 1956 by Edwina C. Rubinstein.

LITTLE, BROWN AND CO. in association with The Atlantic Monthly Press for "More and More" by Margaret Atwood from *The Animals in That Country*, copyright © 1968 by Oxford University Press (Canadian Branch).

LIVERIGHT PUBLISHING CORPORATION for "He Stared at Me" and "Serenade" from *The Path on the Rainbow* edited by George Cronyn, copyright 1918 by Boni & Liveright, copyright 1934 by Liveright Publishing Corporation and "The Graffiti Poet" by Nancy Willard from *Carpenter of the Sun*, copyright © 1974 by Nancy Willard.

ANNETTE LYNCH for "Gratitude."

MCGRAW-HILL BOOK COMPANY for "Advice to a Neighbor Girl," "A Poem Written on a Floating Red Leaf," and "Written at a Party Where My Lord Gave Away a Thousand Bolts of Silk" from *The Orchid Boat*, translated and edited by Kenneth Rexroth and Ling Chung, English translation copyright © 1972 by Kenneth Rexroth and Ling Chung.

MCGRAW-HILL RYERSON LIMITED for "Old Women of Toronto" by Miriam Waddington from *The Season's Lovers*.

Edith Lovejoy Pierce for "Pattern."

Random House, Inc. for "Confession to Settle a Curse" by Rosmarie
   Waldrop from *The Aggressive Ways of a Casual Stranger*,
   copyright © 1972 by Rosmarie Waldrop.

The Regents of the University of California for "Quiet Water" by
   Samiati Alisjahbana, translated by Burton Raffel and
   Nurdin Salam, and "A Woman" by Siti Nuraini, translated by
   James S. Holmes, from *Anthology of Modern Indonesian
   Poetry*, edited by Burton Raffel, published by the University of
   California Press.

Armand Schwerner for "a woman's song, about men" adapted from
   Poemes Eskimos, Victor.

Anne Spencer for "Letter to My Sister."

The Swallow Press, Inc. for "To My Son, Approaching 11" by Linda
   Pastan from *A Perfect Circle of Sun*, © 1971 by Linda Pastan.

University of Missouri Press and the author for "Dear Little Man" by
   Gabriela Mistral from *Swans, Cygnets and Owl* by Mildred E.
   Johnson, copyright 1956 by the Curators of the University
   of Missouri.

The Viking Press, Inc. for "The Practical Clown" by Sandra
   Hochman from *The Vaudeville Marriage*, copyright © 1966 by
   Sandra Hochman; "The Adversary" by Phyllis McGinley
   from *Times Three*, copyright © 1959 by Phyllis McGinley;
   "Song of Perfect Propriety" by Dorothy Parker from *The
   Portable Dorothy Parker*, copyright 1926, copyright renewed
   1954 by Dorothy Parker.

Wesleyan University Press for "Simple-song" by Marge Piercy from
   Hard Loving, copyright © 1969 by Marge Piercy.

Introduction

The poetry in this collection has all been written by women,
and each poem, in some way, presents an aspect of the poet's
image of herself. She sees herself variously as lover,
mother, wife, daughter, and independent being;
frightened, happy, vulnerable, strong. But all the poems, in one
way or another, are about the poet as a woman.

Alone Amid All This Noise is a liberally taken cross-section
of what women poets were writing at different times in different
places. Though it is a broad statement of what was happening
through the centuries, certain patterns can be seen, and the
historical reasons for these patterns.

Up until the eighteenth century, a great deal of the poetry is
by women of the nobility or by women who devoted their lives
to religion. Not only were they, for the most part, the only
literate women, but they were the only ones with the time to write
and the possibility of having their work preserved.

The twentieth-century poets included in *Alone Amid All
This Noise* are principally American and English women.
Women all over the world are writing poetry but it is still
difficult to find English translations of substantial portions
of their work.

The subjects women write about change and broaden through
the centuries. The earliest women poets wrote mostly about
romantic love, since most of their time and energy was devoted
to men. It was only through a relationship with a man that
women had any value or function. So they wrote about being
happy or miserable in love. Of course, women today are still
concerned with romantic love, but no longer exclusively.

In the past but also in this century, women have written a
great deal about aging and the terrible fear of loss of physical
beauty. These feelings were probably generated by their
dependence on men to appreciate them before they could
appreciate themselves.

Today as yesterday women write about their roles as daughters

and as mothers with great tenderness and sensitivity.
Increasingly now, with great vitality, perceptiveness, and clarity,
they write about themselves as separate individuals. They are
concerned with themselves simply as people, not as attachments
to men and children.

Finally, more and more, women are writing with insight
about the subordinate place they have been assigned by centuries
of societies dominated by male points of view, values,
and needs.

Ours is a time of a great outpouring of poetry by women. It is
being published; it is being read. It is a good time to be a
woman; it is a good time to be a poet.

Greece
Sappho (612–557 B.C.)

✍ *A Woman's Plea*

I pray for long life and health.
My children, I would escape
from wrinkles and cling to youth.

✍ *Andromeda, What Now?*

Can this farm girl
in farm-girl finery burn your heart?
She is even ignorant of the way
to lift her gown over her ankles.

✍ *To an Uneducated Woman*

When dead you will lie forever forgotten,
for you have no claim to the Pierian roses.
Dim here, you will move more dimly in Hell,
flitting among the undistinguished dead.

Translated by Willis Barnstone

Greece
Sappho (612–557 B.C.)

 *Headdress*

My mother always said
that in her youth she was
exceedingly in fashion

wearing a purple ribbon
looped in her hair. But
the girl whose hair is yellower

than torchlight need wear no
colorful ribbons from Sardis—
but a garland of fresh flowers.

Translated by Willis Barnstone

Greece
Praxilla (c. 450 B.C.)

 *Of The Sensual World*

Most beautiful of things I leave is sunlight;
then come glazing stars and the moon's face;
then ripe cucumbers and apples and pears.

Translated by Willis Barnstone

❦ *Jesukin*

Jesukin
Lives my little cell within;
What were wealth of cleric high—
All is lie but Jesukin.

Nursling nurtured, as 'tis right,
Harbors here no servile spright,
Jesu of the skies, who art
Next my heart through every night.

Jesukin, my good for aye,
Calling and will not have nay,
King of all things, ever true,
He shall have me who will away.

Jesu, more than angel aid,
Fosterling not formed to fade,
Nursed by me in desert wild,
Jesu, Child of Judah's Maid.

Sons of kings and kingly kin
To my land may enter in;
Guest of none I hope to be
Save of Thee, my Jesukin.

Unto heaven's High King confest
Sing a chorus, maidens blest!
He is o'er us, though within
Jesukin is on our breast.

Translated by George Sigerson

Arabia
The Lady Maisun (c. 650)

✤ *She Scorns Her Husband the Caliph*

A tent with rustling breezes cool
Delights me more than palace high,
And more the cloak of simple wool
Than robes in which I learned to sigh.

The crust I ate beside my tent
Was more than this fine bread to me;
The wind's voice where the hill-path went
Was more than tambourine can be.

And more than purr of friendly cat
I love the watch-dog's bark to hear;
And more than any lubbard fat
I love a Bedouin cavalier!

Translated by R. A. Nicholson

Japan
Lady Ōtomo of Sakanoue (8th Century)

Sent from the Capital to Her Elder Daughter

More than the gems
Locked away and treasured
In his comb-box
By the God of the Sea,
I prize you, my daughter.
But we are of this world
And such is its way!
Summoned by your man,
Obedient, you journeyed
To the far-off land of Koshi.
Since we parted,
Like a spreading vine,
Your eyebrows, pencil-arched,
Like waves about to break,
Have flitted before my eyes,
Bobbing like tiny boats.
Such is my yearning for you
That this body, time-riddled,
May well not bear the strain.

Envoy

Had I only known
My longing would be so great,
Like a clear mirror
I'd have looked on you—
Not missing a day,
Not even an hour.

Translated by Geoffrey Bownas and Anthony Thwaite

Japan
Lady Ōtomo of Sakanoue (8th Century)

You say, "I will come."
And you do not come.
Now you say, "I will not come."
So I shall expect you.
Have I learned to understand you?

Translated by Kenneth Rexroth

My heart, thinking
"How beautiful he is"
Is like a swift river
Which though one dams it and dams it,
Will still break through.

Translated by Arthur Waley

China
Han Ts'ui-p'in (9th Century)

∽ *A Poem Written on a Floating Red Leaf*

How fast this water flows away!
Buried in the women's quarters,
The days pass in idleness.
Red leaf, I order you—
Go find someone
In the world of men.

Translated by Kenneth Rexroth and Ling Chung

China
Yü Hsüan-chi (mid 9th Century)

꩜   *Advice to a Neighbor Girl*

Afraid of the sunlight,
You cover your face with your silk sleeves.
Tired out with Spring melancholy,
You neglect your makeup.
It is easier to get priceless jewels
Than to find a man with a true heart.
Why wet your pillow with secret tears?
Why hide your heartbreak in the flowers?
Go, seek a handsome famous man like Sung Yü.
Don't long for someone who will never come back.

Translated by Kenneth Rexroth and Ling Chung

China
Ch'ien T'ao (early 11th Century)

✆ *Written at a Party Where My Lord Gave Away a Thousand Bolts of Silk*

A bolt of silk for each clear toned song.
Still these beauties do not think it is enough.
Little do they know of a weaving girl,
Sitting cold by her window,
Endlessly throwing her shuttle to and fro.

Translated by Kenneth Rexroth and Ling Chung

Japan
Lady Suwo (11th Century)

That spring night I spent
Pillowed on your arm
Never really happened
Except in a dream.
Unfortunately I am
Talked about anyway.

Translated by Kenneth Rexroth

Persia
Rábi'a, Daughter of Ka'b (12th Century)

 *A Curse*

This is my curse on thee. God send thou love
One like thyself, unkind and obdurate,
That knowing Love's deep cautery thou mayst writhe
In loneliness, and know my worth too late.

Translated by R. A. Nicholson

France
Marie de France (12th Century)

✌ *Would I Might Go Far Over Sea*

Would I might go far over sea,
My Love, or high above the air,
And come to land or heaven with thee,
Where no law is, and none shall be.
Against beholding the most rare
Strange beauty that thou hast for me.

Alas, for, in this bitter land,
Full many a written curse doth stand
Against the kiss thy lips should bear;
Against the sweet gift of thy hands;
Against the knowing that thou art fair,
And too fond loving of thy hair.

Translated by Arthur O'Shaughnessy

ᘒ *I'll Sing, Although I'm Loath to Make This Plea*

A chantar m'er de so qu'eu no volria

I'll sing, although I'm loath to make this plea,
For he I love brought me misery.
There's no one on the earth so dear to me;
But gentleness he scorns, and courtesy.
For all my wit and charms he doesn't care.
More slighted and deceived I couldn't be
If mockery in my eyes you'd seen me bare.

Dear friend, I own a solace in distress.
I never wronged you, as you must confess,
And Seguis surely loved Valensa less.
That I've loved more than you, brings happiness;
For you're the finest lover anywhere.
With pride and cruel answers you transgress
Our love, but smiles for others you can spare.

Dear friend, your pride has struck me with dismay.
Unjustly from my loving side you stray.
Another now has coaxing words to say,
Another smiles and welcomes you today.
Think of the kissing—dawn of our affair—
O God, absolve me from all guilt, I pray!
This parting brings me nothing but despair.

Your bravery has made my heart distressed,
Your matchless worth has snatcht away my rest.
No woman, near or far, with tender breast,
Could fight if you should put her to the test.
But you, who've tasted everything that's rare,
Should quickly recognize which love is best.
Recall the pledging-songs we used to share.

Yes, look at me beyond the lesser throng.
Highborn and beautiful, in truth I'm strong.
I love you. That is why I send along
This faithful message of a loving song.
Sweet gentle friend, I ask you to declare
Why you are callous, why you do me wrong.
O is it pride or malice that you bear?

—Go, find him out, I bid you, and declare
How pride precedes a fall, my warning song.

Translated by Jack Lindsay

In the season when the world leafs and flowers, joy grows for all true lovers; together they go to the gardens where birds sing sweetly. All young men who are not churls fall in love and vie with one another in serving; and every girl knows only joy. But for me there are grief and tears.

For my father has brought me to dismay, and often he hurts me cruelly. He means to give me a husband against my will. And I neither want that nor can I abide it. So, every hour, I am in great torment, and neither flowers nor leaves can cheer me.

Translated by Willard R. Trask

France
Christine de Pisan (1364–1431?)

ℰ *Christine to Her Son*

Son, of great fortune have I none
To make you rich: instead of gold,
Though, certain lessons I would bring
Up, if you'll give them a hearing.

From first youth, innocent and pure,
Learn to know what people are,
And so, by seeing what they're like,
Protect yourself from gross mistake.

Upon the destitute take pity,
Poor creatures you will naked see,
Give them assistance as you may!
Bearing in mind you too will die.

Love him who is a friend to you
And watch out for your enemy:
No one can have too many friends,
There is no minor enemy.

What serves the Lord do not discard
For a world overmuch enslaved:
The worldly go to meet their fate
And the enduring soul holds out.

Translated by Barbara Howes

Italy
Barbara Torelli (1475?–1533)

✍ *On the Murder of Her Husband*

Spent is the torch of Love, broken his dart,
his quiver, and his bow, and all his power,
for cruel death has rooted out the bower
beneath whose tranquil shade I sweetly slept.
Ah, why can I not force the narrow tomb,
and still be with my love, and share his fate—
my gentle sire, who but five days and eight
could dwell with me before his boundless doom?

That gelid frost I'd thaw with all my fire,
and with my tears I would remold that dust,
and breathe new life on it with my desire.
Then, challenging, emboldened, to the one
who severed my dear bond, I so would boast:
"O murderer, Love has such a wonder done."

Translated by Joseph Tusiani

Spain
Santa Teresa d'Avila (1515–1582)

✎ *Bookmark*

Let nothing disturb thee,
Nothing affright thee;
All things are passing;
God never changeth;
Patient endurance
Attaineth to all things;
Who God possesseth
In nothing is wanting;
Alone God sufficeth.

Translated by Henry Wadsworth Longfellow

Italy
Gaspara Stampa (1523?–1554)

O wicked tyrant, send me back my heart,
which you so wrongly hold and tear to shreds,
and do to it and me that very thing
which to a hind lions and tigers do.
Eight days have passed, one entire year to me,
with neither news nor messages from you—
contrary to the oath you swore to me,
my Count, O spring of valor and deceit.

Why, do you think me Hercules or Samson
able to bear so much distress and smart—
me, young, a woman, with my wits all gone
and, worse than that, left here without my heart,
and without you, from whom I used to draw
all vigor and all strength, to shelter me?

Translated by Joseph Tusiani

France
Louise Labé (c. 1524–1566)

ℰ *The Eighth Sonnet*

I live, I die. I drown, I am aflame.
I shake with cold and perish with the heat.
I leap from anguish to delight; from sweet
To bitter. No two moments are the same,

And all the leap of joy and lunge of gloom
Join in a single instant. Each delight
Aches with a hidden torment, and the night
Fades, yet survives. I wither, yet I bloom.

So Eros leads me on. And when at last
I know the full extremity of pain,
I feel, quite suddenly, at ease again,

Strangely at peace. And when once more I see
Some future hope, some present certainty,
He comes and flings the furies of the past!

Translated by Frederic Prokosch

✺ *When I Was Fair and Young*

When I was fair and young, and favor gracèd me,
  Of many was I sought, their mistress for to be;
But I did scorn them all, and answered them therefore,
   Go, go, go, seek some otherwhere,
    Impórtune me no more!

How many weeping eyes I made to pine with woe,
  How many sighing hearts, I have no skill to show;
Yet I the prouder grew, and answered them therefore,
   Go, go, go, seek some otherwhere,
    Impórtune me no more!

Then spake fair Venus' son, that proud victorious boy,
  And said: Fine dame, since that you be so coy,
I will so pluck your plumes that you shall say no more,
   Go, go, go, seek some otherwhere,
    Impórtune me no more!

When he had spake these words, such change grew in my breast
  That neither night nor day since that, I could take any rest.
Then lo! I did repent that I had said before,
   Go, go, go, seek some otherwhere,
    Impórtune me no more!

↻ *Prayer before Execution*

O merciful Father, my hope is in Thee!
O gracious Redeemer, deliver Thou me!
My bondage bemoaning, with sorrowful groaning,
I long to be free;
Lamenting, relenting, and humbly repenting,
O Jesu, my Saviour, I languish for Thee.

Version of John Fawcett, 1782.

America
Anne Bradstreet (1612–1672)

ᔒ "*To My dear and loving Husband*"

If ever two were one, then surely we.
If ever man were lov'd by wife, then thee;
If ever wife was happy in a man,
Compare with me ye women if you can.
I prize thy love more then whole Mines of gold,
Or all the riches that the East doth hold.
My love is such that Rivers cannot quench,
Nor ought but love from thee, give recompence.
Thy love is such I can no way repay,
The heavens reward thee manifold I pray.
Then while we live, in love lets so persever,
That when we live no more, we may live ever.

England
Margaret, Duchess of Newcastle (1624–1674)

O do not grieve, Dear Heart, nor shed a tear,
Since in your eyes my life doth all appear;
And in your buried countenance my death I find;
I'm buried in your melancholy mind.

But in your smiles, I'm glorified to rise,
And your pure love doth me eternalize:
Thus by your favour you a god me make,
When in your hate a devil's shape I take.

ᔕ *Epitaph on the Monument of Sir William Dyer at Colmworth, 1641*

My dearest dust, could not thy hasty day
Afford thy drowszy patience leave to stay
One hower longer: so that we might either
Sate up, or gone to bedd together?
But since thy finisht labor hath possest
Thy weary limbs with early rest,
Enjoy it sweetly: and thy widdowe bride
Shall soone repose her by thy slumbring side.
Whose business, now, is only to prepare
My nightly dress, and call to prayre:
Mine eyes wax heavy and ye day growes cold.
Draw, draw ye closed curtaynes: and make room:
My deare, my dearest dust; I come, I come.

Persia
Princess Zeb-un-Nissa (1639–1689)

↺ *Lament*

Within my bosom stirs once more tonight
A voice of song. Love, erstwhile slumbering,
Intones his mystery, and the flowers of spring
Relive and bloom. Winter, forbear to smite
My heart's late flowers. Listen! From left and right
Through the green boughs the bulbul's note is heard,
And, wing-clipt and imprisoned, my heart's bird
Flutters against his barriers, wild for flight.

Translated by Paul Whalley

✆ *The Defiance*

By Heaven 'tis false, I am not vain;
    And rather would the subject be
Of your indifference, or disdain,
    Than wit or raillery.

Take back the trifling praise you give,
    And pass it on some other fool,
Who may the injuring wit believe,
    That turns her into ridicule.

Tell her, she's witty, fair, and gay,
    With all the charms that can subdue:
Perhaps she'll credit what you say;
    But curse me if I do.

If your diversion you design,
    On my good-nature you have prest:
Or if you do intend it mine,
    You have mistook the jest.

ॐ *When Maidens Are Young*

When maidens are young, and in their spring,
Of pleasure, of pleasure, let 'em take their full swing,
    Full swing, full swing,
And love, and dance, and play, and sing,
For Silvia, believe it, when youth is done,
There's naught but hum-drum, hum-drum, hum-drum,
There's naught but hum-drum, hum-drum, hum-drum.

ॐ *Foolish Men*

Foolish men, who do accuse
Women without reason,
Without seeing that you are the cause
Of the very thing you blame.

If with ardor without compare
You woo them when they reject you,
Why do you expect them to behave well
When you incite them to do wrong?

You break down their resistance,
And then gravely
You declare that it was levity on their part
What your persistence achieved.

Translated by Seymour Resnick

☙ *To Her Portrait*

This trickery of paint which you perceive
With all the finest hues of art enwrought,
Which is false argument of colors taught
By subtle means the senses to deceive—

This by which foolish woman would believe
She could undo the evil years have brought
And conquering in the war against time fought
Could triumph over age, and youth retrieve—

Is all a futile ruse that she has tried,
A fragile flower tossed against the wind,
A useless bribe the power of fate to appease,

A silly effort of mistaken pride,
A base desire, and viewed in rightful mind,
Is dust, a corpse, a shade—is less than these.

Translated by Beatrice Gilman Proske

✑ *To Dr. Swift on his Birthday,*
30th November 1721

St. Patrick's Dean, your country's pride,
My early and my only guide,
You taught how I might youth prolong,
By knowing what was right and wrong;
How from my heart to bring supplies
Of lustre to my fading eyes;
How soon a beauteous mind repairs
The loss of changed or falling hairs;
How wit and virtue from within
Send out a smoothness o'er the skin:
Your lectures could my fancy fix,
And I can please at thirty-six.
The sight of Chloe at fifteen,
Coquetting, gives me not the spleen;
The idol now of every fool
Till time shall make their passions cool;
Then tumbling down Time's steepy hill,
While Stella holds her station still.

ℰ *To Her Husband, at the Wedding*

The persimmon, lo!
No one can tell till he tastes it!
   Marriage is even so.

Translated by Curtis Hidden Page

ℰ *On Her Child's Death*

I wonder in what fields today
He chases dragon-flies in play,
My little boy—who ran away.

Translated by Curtis Hidden Page

Marie-Françoise-Catherine de Beauveau,
la Marquise de Boufflers (1711–1786)

🌀 *Air: Sentir Avec Ardeur*

Say what you will in two
Words and get through.
Long, frilly
Palaver is silly.

Know how to read? you *must*
Before you can write. An idiot
Will always
Talk a lot.

You need not always narrate;
    cite; date,
But listen a while and not say: "I! I!"
Want to know why?

The *me* is tyrannical;
        academical.
Early, late
Boredom's cognate mate
    in step at his side
And I with a *me*, I fear,
                    yet again!

Say what you will in two
Words and get through!
Long, frilly
Palaver is silly.

Translated by Ezra Pound

☙ *On Being Brought from Africa to America*

'Twas mercy brought me from my *Pagan* land,
Taught my benighted soul to understand
That there's a God, that there's a *Saviour* too:
Once I redemption neither sought nor knew.
Some view our sable race with scornful eye,
"Their colour is a diabolic die."
Remember, *Christians*, *Negroes*, black as *Cain*,
May be refin'd, and join th' angelic train.

ↄ *Serenade*

O
   to be a man!

ↄ *He Stared at Me*

My dear friend
   your husband,
   at me
   how he stared.
Will you throw him away?

American Indian
Kiowa Girl (19th Century)

〰 *Warpath Song*

Ah, I never, never can forget
The playful word you spoke long since.
This man who seeks to marry me,
He with his sore-backed ponies,
    What's he to me!

〰 *Wind Song*

Idlers and cowards are here at home now,
Whenever they wish, they see their beloved ones.
Oh, idlers and cowards are here at home now,
But the youth I love is gone to war, far hence.
Weary, lonely, for me he longs.

American Indian
Sioux Woman (19th Century)

〰 *You May Go on the Warpath*

You may go on the warpath;
When your name I hear [announced among the victors]
Then I will marry you.

Eskimo
Anonymous (19th Century)

ᘓ A Woman's Song, about Men

first I lowered my head
and for a start I stared at the ground
for a second I couldn't say anything
but now that they're gone
I raise my head I look straight ahead I can answer
They say I stole a man
the husband of one of my aunts
they say I took him for a husband of my own
lies
fairy tales
slander
It was him, he
lay down next to me
But they're men
which is why they lie
that's the reason
and it's my hard luck.

Translated by Armand Schwerner

ᐒ from *Sonnets from the Portuguese*

If thou must love me, let it be for naught
Except for love's sake only. Do not say,
"I love her for her smile—her look—her way
Of speaking gently—for a trick of thought
That falls in well with mine, and certes brought
A sense of pleasant ease on such a day"—
For these things in themselves, Belovèd, may
Be changed, or change for thee—and love, so wrought,
May be unwrought so. Neither love me for
Thine own dear pity's wiping my cheeks dry:
A creature might forget to weep, who bore
Thy comfort long, and lose thy love thereby!
But love me for love's sake, that evermore
Thou may'st love on, through love's eternity.

✆ *Youth Gone*

Youth gone, and beauty gone if ever there
    Dwelt beauty in so poor a face as this;
    Youth gone and beauty, what remains of bliss?
I will not bind fresh roses in my hair,
To shame a cheek at best but little fair,—
    Leave youth his roses, who can bear a thorn,—
I will not seek for blossoms anywhere,
    Except such common flowers as blow with corn.

Youth gone and beauty gone, what doth remain?
    The longing of a heart pent up forlorn,
        A silent heart whose silence loves and longs;
        The silence of a heart which sang its songs
    While youth and beauty made a summer morn,
Silence of love that cannot sing again.

The Hope I Dreamed of

The hope I dreamed of was a dream,
  Was but a dream. And now I wake
Exceeding comfortless, and worn, and old,
    For a dream's sake.

I hang my harp upon a tree,
  A weeping willow in a lake;
I hang my silenced harp there, wrung and snapt,
    For a dream's sake.

Lie still, lie still, my breaking heart;
  My silent heart, lie still and break.
Life, and the world, and mine own self, are changed
    For a dream's sake.

ꙮ *I Never Hear the Word "Escape"*

I never hear the word "escape"
Without a quicker blood,
A sudden expectation,
A flying attitude.

I never hear of prisons broad
By soldiers battered down,
But I tug childish at my bars,—
Only to fail again!

ꙮ *I'm Wife*

I'm wife: I've finished that,
That other state;
I'm Czar, I'm woman now:
It's safer so.

How odd the girl's life looks
Behind this soft eclipse!
I think that earth seems so
To those in heaven now.

This being comfort, then
That other kind was pain;
But why compare?
I'm wife! stop there!

✌ *She Rose to His Requirement*

She rose to his requirement, dropped
The playthings of her life
To take the honorable work
Of woman and of wife.

If aught she missed in her new day
Of amplitude, or awe,
Or first prospective, or the gold
In using wore away,

It lay unmentioned, as the sea
Develops pearl and weed,
But only to himself is known
The fathoms they abide.

Spain
Rosalía de Castro (1837–1885)

ℰ *I Love You ... Why Do You Hate Me?*

I love you ... Why do you hate me?
—I hate you ... Why do you love me?
Saddest, most mysterious
Secret of the spirit is this.

And yet it is a truth, hard
As truth in a torturer's hand!
—You hate me, because I love you;
I love you, because you hate me.

Translated by Edwin Morgan

✍ *They Say That the Plants Do Not Speak*

They say that the plants do not speak, nor the brooks, nor
   the birds,
Nor the waves with their roar, nor with their brilliance
   the stars.
So they say; but one cannot be sure, for always, when I
   go by,

They whisper about me and say
            —Ah, there goes the madwoman, dreaming
Of the everlasting springtide of life and the fields,
And yet soon, very soon, her hair will be gray,
And trembling, frozen, she sees that the frost is upon the
   grass.

Translated by Kate Flores

Canada
Annie Louisa Walker (c. 1850)

 Song

"WOMEN'S RIGHTS" CONVENTION

Our husbands they may scold or snore,
    Or bake, or fry, or stew;
While we this man-spoiled world restore,
    And make it good as new.

No husband's mission own we now,
    To bully or to bore;
"Obedience" of the marriage vow,
    Shall form a part no more.
                                PUNCH

Maid of France! whose armèd hand
Saved of old thy native land;
Lady! on thy castle wall
Aiding, cheering, leading all;
Ye, and hundred names beside
Shining through war's crimson tide,
Show that *we* can rule the fight,—
Show, command is Woman's Right!

Wit, her female votaries claims,
Learning guards their honoured names;
Art and Poetry have found
Women to their service bound;
History's voice aloud declares
Choicest gifts were ever theirs;
Why should *we* then wear the chain?
Let us have our Rights again!

Home affections! peaceful hours!
Fireside joys, that once were ours;
Vain delusions! meant to keep
Women's souls from loftier sweep,
We have cast you all away.
Husbands, children, what are they?
Ours no more each household task,
Injured Women's Rights we ask!

Ꮬ *"And He Said, Fight On"*

(Tennyson)

Time and its ally, Dark Disarmament,
    Have compassed me about,
Have massed their armies, and on battle bent
    My forces put to rout;
But though I fight alone, and fall, and die,
    Talk terms of Peace? Not I.

They war upon my fortress, and their guns
    Are shattering its walls;
My army plays the cowards' part, and runs.
    Pierced by a thousand balls;
They call for my surrender. I reply,
    "Give quarter now? Not I."

They've shot my flag to ribbons, but in rents
    It floats above the height;
Their ensign shall not crown my battlements
    While I can stand and fight.
I fling defiance at them as I cry,
    "Capitulate? Not I."

Germany
Else Lasker-Schüler (1869–1945)

♋ *Over Shining Shingle*

O to go home at last—
The lights fade fast—
Their final greeting gone.

Where lay my head?
Mother, say soon.
Our garden, too, is dead.

A bunch of grey carnations lies
In some lost corner of the house.
Every ounce it took of all our care,

It wreathed the welcome at the door,
And gave itself, in color generous,
O mother dear.

It spread the sunset gold,
And in the morning soft desires,
Before this downfall of the world.

None of my sisters live now and no brothers live.
Winter has played with death in every nest
And frozen cold our every song of love.

Translated by Christopher Middleton

℧ *Gold Ladies*

(Painted on Chinese Parchment)

"Ready or not, you must be caught,
Hiding around the goal or not!"

The children shout in Hide-and-Seek:
    The dainty ladies, jewel-bright,
In robes of flame and gold bedight
    With parted lips would seem to speak:

"Playmates, we hid so near our goal—
    Our old gay life—O days all spent!
Unready were we when we went
    Trapped unawares, with frightened soul.

" 'Home free!' Who's free? How vain a thought!
    Gold Ladies (so you call us, dears,)
Play Hide-and-Seek adown all years.
    We—such as we—are always—'Caught!' "

    "Ready or not, ready or not. . . .
    Hiding around the goal or not. . . ."

⟨§⟩ *A Decade*

When you came, you were like red wine and honey,
And the taste of you burnt my mouth with its sweetness.
Now you are like morning bread,
Smooth and pleasant.
I hardly taste you at all, for I know your savor;
But I am completely nourished.

America
Anne Spencer (1882?–   )

⟨℧⟩ *Letter to My Sister*

It is dangerous for a woman to defy the gods;
To taunt them with the tongue's thin tip,
Or strut in the weakness of mere humanity,
Or draw a line daring them to cross;
The gods who own the searing lightning,
The drowning waters, the tormenting fears,
The anger of red sins . . .
Oh, but worse still if you mince along timidly—
Dodge this way or that, or kneel, or pray,
Or be kind, or sweat agony drops,
Or lay your quick body over your feeble young,
If you have beauty or plainness, if celibate,
Or vowed—the gods are Juggernaut,
Passing over each of us . . .
    Or this you may do:
Lock your heart, then quietly,
And, lest they peer within,
Light no lamp when dark comes down.
Raise no shade for sun,
Breathless must your breath come thru,
If you'd die and dare deny
The gods their godlike fun!

U.S.A.-Israel
Jessie Sampter (1883–1938)

↺ *Kadia the Young Mother Speaks*

*who was born in a Judaean village
of parents from Yemen, Arabia*

Baby,
You shall be free:
You shall not be sold into service as I was (a mere child),
You shall not be sold into marriage as our mother was (a mere
    child).

You beautiful thing!
You shall be free to be beautiful,
Not a poor starved sickly baby as I was,
Wrapped in rags, with sore eyes,
Not pitiable, ashamed to have been born a girl,
As the chattel women of the East are humbled,
But proud in your womanhood, as I am now,
Baby.

Baby, Baby,
Here in our land where all babies are born equal and free,
You shall hold on to your freedom,
You shall not lose sight of it with your big eyes.
You shall learn, learn, and be gentle, wise and always loving,
But nevertheless free,
Always free, wholly free,
Baby!

↶ *Meditation at Kew*

Alas! for all the pretty women who marry dull men,
Go into the suburbs and never come out again,
Who lose their pretty faces, and dim their pretty eyes,
Because no one has skill or courage to organize.

What do these pretty women suffer when they marry?
They bear a boy who is like Uncle Harry,
A girl, who is like Aunt Eliza, and not new,
These old, dull races must breed true.

I would enclose a common in the sun,
And let the young wives out to laugh and run;
I would steal their dull clothes and go away,
And leave the pretty naked things to play.

Then I would make a contract with hard Fate
That they see all the men in the world and choose a mate,
And I would summon all the pipers in the town
That they dance with Love at a feast, and dance him down.

From the gay unions of choice
We'd have a race of splendid beauty, and of thrilling voice.
The World whips frank, gay love with rods,
But frankly, gayly shall we get the gods.

✆ *Central Park at Dusk*

Buildings above the leafless trees
   Loom high as castles in a dream,
While one by one the lamps come out
   To thread the twilight with a gleam.

There is no sign of leaf or bud,
   A hush is over everything—
Silent as women wait for love,
   The world is waiting for the spring.

ᕙ *The Old Maid*

I saw her in a Broadway car,
  The woman I might grow to be;
I felt my lover look at her
  And then turn suddenly to me.

Her hair was dull and drew no light
  And yet its color was as mine;
Her eyes were strangely like my eyes
  Tho' love had never made them shine.

Her body was a thing grown thin,
  Hungry for love that never came;
Her soul was frozen in the dark
  Unwarmed forever by love's flame.

I felt my lover look at her
  And then turn suddenly to me,—
His eyes were magic to defy
  The woman I shall never be.

✿ *Let No Charitable Hope*

Now let no charitable hope
Confuse my mind with images
Of eagle and of antelope:
I am in nature none of these.

I was, being human, born alone;
I am, being woman, hard beset;
I live by squeezing from a stone
The little nourishment I get.

In masks outrageous and austere
The years go by in single file;
But none has merited my fear,
And none has quite escaped my smile.

ℰ *Where, O, Where?*

I need not die to go
So far you cannot know
My escape, my retreat,
And the prints of my feet
Written in blood or dew;
They shall be hid from you,
In fern-seed lost
Or the soft flakes of frost.
They will turn somewhere
Under water, over air,
To earth space or stellar,
Or the garret or cellar
Of the house next door;
You shall see me no more
Though each night I hide
In your bed, at your side.

America
Marianne Moore (1886–1972)

✺ *Silence*

My father used to say,
'Superior people never make long visits,
have to be shown Longfellow's grave
or the glass flowers at Harvard.
Self-reliant like the cat—
that takes its prey to privacy,
the mouse's limp tail hanging like a shoelace from its mouth—
they sometimes enjoy solitude,
and can be robbed of speech
by speech which has delighted them.
The deepest feeling always shows itself in silence;
not in silence, but restraint.'
Nor was he insincere in saying, 'Make my house your inn'.
Inns are not residences.

ᘒ *The Suppliant*

Long have I beat with timid hands upon life's leaden door,
Praying the patient, futile prayer my fathers prayed before,
Yet I remain without the close, unheeded and unheard,
And never to my listening ear is borne the waited word.

Soft o'er the threshold of the years there comes this counsel cool:
The strong demand, contend, prevail; the beggar is a fool!

ᘒ *The Heart of a Woman*

The heart of a woman goes forth with the dawn,
As a lone bird, soft winging, so restlessly on,
Afar o'er life's turrets and vales does it roam
In the wake of those echoes the heart calls home.

The heart of a woman falls back with the night,
And enters some alien cage in its plight,
And tries to forget it has dreamed of the stars,
While it breaks, breaks, breaks on the sheltering bars.

She Warns Him

I am a lamp, a lamp that is out;
   I am a shallow stream;
In it are neither pearls or trout,
    Nor one of the things that you dream.

Why do you smile and deny, my lover?
   I will not be denied.
I am a book, a book with a cover,
    And nothing at all inside.

Here is the truth, and you must grapple,
   Grapple with what I have said.
I am a dumpling without any apple,
    I am a star that is dead.

Russia
Anna Akhmatova (1888–1966)

℧ *You Are Always New*

You are always new and always hidden;
More each day I yield to your desire.
But your love, hard-hearted friend, has bidden
Me to tests of iron and of fire.

You forbid my song, forbid my laughter,
Long ago you told me not to pray.
But I care not for what happens after
If from you I am not cast away.

From the earth and skies you would me sever;
I live, and my songs have ceased to swell.
'Tis as if to my free soul for ever
You had shut both Paradise and Hell.

Translated by C. M. Bowra

♘ *The White Bird*

Tender he was, perplexed and jealous; yet
    He loved me like God's sun; my heart was stirred.
Because it sang of days before we met,
    He killed my white-winged bird.

He came at sunset to my room and said:
    Write poems, darling, laugh and love with me.
By the round well my happy bird lies dead
    Beneath the alder tree.

I promised him I would not cry nor care;
    But then my heart became a stony thing.
And now it seems that always, everywhere,
    I hear my sweet bird sing.

Translated by Frances Cornford and E. P. Salaman

America
Celia Dropkin (1888–1956)

〰 *Poem*

You sowed in me, not a child
but yourself.
So it's you growing in me daily,
greater and more distinct.
There's no room left inside me
for myself
and my soul lies like a dog at your feet
growing fainter and fainter.
But, dying into you,
I still, even now, can make you songs.

Translated from the Yiddish by Adrienne Rich

✑ *Rocking*

The sea its thousands of waves
Divinely rocks.
Listening to the loving seas
I rock my child.

The wind wandering in the night
Rocks the fields of wheat.
Listening to the loving winds
I rock my child.

God in Heaven His thousands of worlds
Rocks without noise.
Feeling His hand in the dark
I rock my child.

Translated by Seymour Resnick

Chile
Gabriela Mistral (1889–1957)

ℰ *Dear Little Man*

O my dear little man, O my dear little man,
Free your canary, as it wants to fly away;
For I am your canary my dear little man,
O let me hop and play.

I went inside your cage, O my dear little man,
O little man, within whose cage I now am penned.
I call you "little," for you do not comprehend me,
Will never comprehend.

Nor am I comprehending you, but in the meantime
Please open that cage door, as I wish liberty;
O my dear little man, I loved you half an hour,
So ask no more from me.

Translated by Mildred E. Johnson

Russia-Israel
Rachel Blumstein (1890–1931)

✆ *Dawn*

A jug of water in the hand, and on
My shoulder—basket, spade, and rake.
To distant fields,—to toil—my path I make.

Upon my right, the great hills fling
Protecting arms; before me—the wide fields!
And in my heart, my twenty Aprils sing . . .

Be this my lot, until I be undone:
Dust of thy road, my land, and thy
Grain waving golden in the sun!

Translated from the Hebrew by Abraham M. Klein

ℭ *Women Have Loved Before*

Women have loved before as I love now;
At least, in lively chronicles of the past—
Of Irish waters by a Cornish prow
Or Trojan waters by a Spartan mast
Much to their cost invaded—here and there,
Hunting the amorous line, skimming the rest,
I find some woman bearing as I bear
Love like a burning city in the breast.
I think however that of all alive
I only in such utter, ancient way
Do suffer love; in me alone survive
The unregenerate passions of a day
When treacherous queens, with death upon the tread,
Heedless and wilful, took their knights to bed.

The Courage that My Mother Had

The courage that my mother had
Went with her, and is with her still:
Rock from New England quarried;
Now granite in a granite hill.

The golden brooch my mother wore
She left behind for me to wear;
I have no thing I treasure more:
Yet, it is something I could spare.

Oh, if instead she'd left to me
The thing she took into the grave!—
That courage like a rock, which she
Has no more need of, and I have.

Argentina
Alfonsina Storni (1892–1938)

✺ She Who Understands

Her dark head fallen forward in her grief,
The beauteous woman kneels in suppliant fashion—
A woman past her youth; the dying Christ
From the stern rood looks on her with compassion.

A burden of vast sadness in her eyes,
Beneath her heart a child, a burden human.
Before the white Christ bleeding there she prays:
"Lord, do not let my child be born a woman!"

Translated by Alice Stone Blackwell

America
Dorothy Parker (1893–1967)

✺ Song of Perfect Propriety

Oh, I should like to ride the seas,
    A roaring buccaneer;
A cutlass banging at my knees,
    A dirk behind my ear.
And when my captives' chains would clank
    I'd howl with glee and drink,
And then fling out the quivering plank
    And watch the beggars sink.

I'd like to straddle gory decks,
    And dig in laden sands,
And know the feel of throbbing necks
    Between my knotted hands.
Oh, I should like to strut and curse
    Among my blackguard crew. . . .
But I am writing little verse,
    As little ladies do.

Oh, I should like to dance and laugh
    And pose and preen and sway,
And rip the hearts of men in half,
    And toss the bits away.
I'd like to view the reeling years
    Through unastonished eyes,
And dip my finger-tips in tears,
    And give my smiles for sighs.

I'd stroll beyond the ancient bounds,
    And tap at fastened gates,
And hear the prettiest of sounds—
    The clink of shattered fates.
My slaves I'd like to bind with thongs
    That cut and burn and chill. . . .
But I am writing little songs,
    As little ladies will.

✌ *Moving*

After the fretful hours were done—
Morning, noon, and afternoon,
After dusk had come, too soon,
And the sun,
A flushed, speechless creditor,
Upon our lack
Had turned a hasty back,
I turned my own
Upon small swarming trifles and edged fears,
To face their residue from other years.

Going from an old house to a new
Gives one curious things to do—
Closets to empty,
Heartaches to throw away,
Threadbare joy
To divest of mothballs,
Papers to destroy:
Letters from golden lads and girls who say
They have come home from the university
With nothing learned but what they were not taught,
Or, they are in love again,
Or, they are sad
Because of too little love and too much thought,
Or, asking what was meant on such a day
When a certain person said
The sort of thing people will say . . .
It doesn't matter.

Some of them are dead,
And some are married, and a few
Are famous.
Going from an old house to a new
Gives one tiring things to do.

And when we leave that new house, as we must,
Maybe, after some yet unlived years,
Shall I look back
To this night, and call myself a fool
For having cried in my heart for the old school
And the university
And the lovers and friends
Lost in the dark forest of the world?
Ambitions shrink;
Time pulls the best awry;
And ends
Come harder as we grow older.
The nights grow colder—
Or do I?

✆ *The Empresses*

Victoria, Carlota, and Eugénie,
were young queens once, were once young empresses,
with ears pierced for their jewels and flower-shaped bonnets
and parasols and billowing bright dresses.

They had young husbands once, with narrow waists
and brave mustaches. They drove satin horses
through shaded parks, and with small smiles presided
at dinners of innumerable courses.

Proud! They were proud, those lovely princesses:
Victoria was determined as a stone,
Eugénie bore the blood of Montezuma,
Carlota gambled for a windy throne.

One won, two lost, all three grew very old,
old women who, before at last they died,
had turned to legends, wearing on their fingers,
like rings, the wars demanded by their pride.

America
Edith Lovejoy Pierce (1904–   )

 *Pattern*

She was there before Caesar's day
And she is still there,
The woman at the doorway, watching.
The man walks off, self-conscious in his new clothes;
He turns around once and tries to grin.
She is not quite sure about his saving the nation,
Or the empire, or freedom, or the world.
Sowing seeds, pitching hay—ah yes, he was good at that
The wind blows, and prying fingers of rain
Meddle with the listless autumn leaves.
The woman turns to face the familiar room
That has died during the last five minutes.
Life narrows into a thin cold draft of loneliness,
Even while she fondles the little boy,
Quiet and awed at her side.
The late rose on the kitchen table drops its petals one by one.

America
Phyllis McGinley (1905–   )

 *The Adversary*

A mother's hardest to forgive.
Life is the fruit she longs to hand you,
Ripe on a plate. And while you live,
Relentlessly she understands you.

Canada
Anne Wilkinson (1910–1961)

ↄ   *Summer Acres*

I

These acres breathe my family,
Holiday with seventy summers' history.
My blood lives here,
Sunned and veined three generations red
Before my bones were formed.

My eyes are wired to the willow
That wept for my father,
My heart is boughed by the cedar
That covers with green limbs the bones of my children,
My hands are white with a daisy, sired
By the selfsame flower my grandfather loved;

My ears are tied to the tattle of water
That echoes the vows of ancestral lovers,
My skin is washed by a lather of waves
That bathed the blond bodies of uncles and aunts
And curled on the long flaxen hair of my mother;

My feet step softly on descendants of grass
That was barely brushed
By the wary boots of a hummingbird woman,
The Great Great Grandmother
Of my mid-century children.

II

September born, reared in the sunset hour,
I was the child of old men heavy with honour;
I mourned the half-mast time of their death and sorrowed
A season for leaves, shaking their scarlet flags
From green virility of trees.

As ears spring cartilaged from skulls
So my ears spring from the sound of water
And the whine of autumn in the family tree.
How tired, how tall grow the trees
When the trees and the family are temples
Whose columns will tumble, leaf over root to their ruin.

Here, in my body's home my heart dyes red
The last hard maple in their acres.
Where birch and elm and willow turn,
Gently bred, to gold against the conifers,
I hail my fathers, sing their blood to the leaf.

✌ *After Four Years*

How to lay down her death,
Bring her back living
Into the open heart, the over-grieving,
Bury once and for all the starving breath,
And lay down her death?

Not on love's breast
Lay down this heavy prize
And close at last the open, the gray eyes
Of her who in my woe can find no rest—
Not on love's breast.

And not in solitude
Lay the long burden down,
For she is there awake when I'm alone,
Who cannot sleep, yet sorely, sorely would—
Oh, not in solitude!

Now everywhere I'm blind;
On the far journeys
Toward the magical old trees and cities
It's the same rooted sorrow that I find,
And everywhere I'm blind.

Is there a human prayer
That might unknot prolonged
Unnatural grief, grief that has surely wronged
Her very radiant presence in the air,
Is there a human prayer?

It is poor love, I know,
Mother and marvelous friend,
Over that final poverty to bend
And not remember all the rich life too:
It is poor love, I know.

"Rich love, come in,
Come home, my treasure.
All that you were and that no word can measure
Melt itself through me like a healing balm,
Rich love, come home."

And here lay down at last
Her long hard death,
And let her be in joy, be ash, not breath,
And let her gently go into the past,
Dear world, to rest at last.

America
May Sarton (1912–   )

✑ *My Father's Death*

After the laboring birth, the clean stripped hull
Glides down the ways and is gently set free,
The landlocked, launched; the cramped made bountiful—
Oh, grave great moment when ships take the sea!
Alone now in my life, no longer child,
This hour and its flood of mystery,
Where death and love are wholly reconciled,
Launches the ship of all my history.
Accomplished now is the last struggling birth,
I have slipped out from the embracing shore
Nor look for comfort to maternal earth.
I shall not be a daughter any more,
But through this final parting, all stripped down,
Launched on the tide of love, go out full grown.

✌ *Narrative*

A woman grew, with waiting, over-quiet.
The earth along its spiralled path was spun
through many a day and night, now green, now dun;
at times she laughed, and then, at times, she cried.

The years went by. By turns she woke and slept
through the long hours of night, but every day
she went, as women go, her casual way,
and no one knew what patient tryst she kept.

Hope and despair tread their alternate round
and merge into acceptance, till at length
the years have only quietness in store.

And so at last the narrative has found
in her its happy end: this tranquil strength
is better than the thing she's waiting for.

Translated by the poet

☯ *Portrait*

It was a heartfelt game, when it began—
polish and cook and sew and mend, contrive,
move between sink and stove, keep flower-beds weeded—
all her love needed was that it was needed,
and merely living kept the blood alive.

Now an old habit leads from sink to stove,
mends and keeps clean the house that looks like home,
and waits in hunger dressed to look like love
for the calm return of those who, when they come,
remind her: this was a game, when it began.

✎ *Old Women of Toronto*

All old women sometimes come to this:
They go to live away, they cross ravines,
Mornings they ride the subway, later look below
To read the red of dogwood and the print of snow.
They tread upon the contours of each month
With delicate feet that hardly sense its shape,
Explore the mouth of March and with a hiss
They spit at myth and swallow counter-bliss.

Their brows beetle, their plush hats tremble,
They specially deplore without preamble
The palomino carpets on the lawns
Steaming with manure in frosty air.
Against all evidence and witnesses they'll swear
They never argued once, or schemed to take
The room in front with the old Morris chair,
And partial view, at least, of the bright lake.

America
Gwendolyn Brooks (1917–   )

✑ *a song in the front yard*

I've stayed in the front yard all my life.
I want a peek at the back
Where it's rough and untended and hungry weed grows.
A girl gets sick of a rose.

I want to go in the back yard now
And maybe down the alley,
To where the charity children play.
I want a good time today.

They do some wonderful things.
They have some wonderful fun.
My mother sneers, but I say it's fine
How they don't have to go in at quarter to nine.
My mother, she tells me that Johnnie Mae
Will grow up to be a bad woman.
That George'll be taken to Jail soon or late
(On account of last winter he sold our back gate).

But I say it's fine. Honest, I do.
And I'd like to be a bad woman, too,
And wear the brave stockings of night-black lace
And strut down the streets with paint on my face.

↩ *The Empty Woman*

The empty woman took toys!
　　In her sisters' homes
Were little girls and boys.

The empty woman had hats
To show. With feathers. Wore combs
In polished waves. Wooed cats

And pigeons. Shopped.
Shopped hard for nephew-toys,
Niece-toys. Made taffy. Popped

Popcorn and hated her sisters,
Featherless and waveless but able to
Mend measles, nag noses, blast blisters

And all day waste wordful girls
And war-boys, and all day
Say "Oh God!"—and tire among curls

And plump legs and proud muscle
And blackened school-bags, babushkas, torn socks,
And bouffants that bustle, and rustle.

☙ An Old Snapshot

Who is this child, alone
In a waste of sand and sea?
Can hers be the flesh and bone
That scaffold me?

In that far summer I know
She saw the horizon clear,
And the sun go down below
As I do, here,

And she felt through her fingers fall
The drifting silt of time
Who exists now—if at all—
In tearless rhyme;

And I ask myself, as I stare
At the photo of sand and sea:
Is it I who am captured there,
Or she here, in me?

✆ *Gratitude*

And should I thank you, my dear skin,
For holding me in,
For holding me in?

When all the while I want to shout
Let me out,
Let me out!

✆ *Vacant Possession*

All day on the phone. All day
desperate for vacant possession,
ringing to find if the furniture has gone
have I moved it yet; if not, why?

How can I explain
that my dead mother's best bedroom and fireside suite
have first claim, that their obstinate
will is to remain. Proud beasts they stand.
Nothing will shift them out
but the voice my mother used when she spoke to her
companionable furniture.

Now her voice is gone and the house is sold and I do not know
the command that persuades a well-loved fireside suite
meekly to rise up on its casters and go!

✺ *The Marriage*

My mother
had eyes
in the back
of her head
the better
to see you with
she said.
A mouth had
my father
all round
and red
a mouth full
of kisses
a hunger outright
for beefsteak
for oysters
three to a bite
and died with it open.
The doctors
that night
tore my small mother
whose front eyes
had shed
a teacup of tears
on his face
from the bed
from his mouth
a dry hole
unstuffed of
his being.

Daytimes
resisting
and nightly
agreeing
I am looked into still
by those back eyes
unseeing.

✆ *Her Kind*

I have gone out, a possessed witch,
haunting the black air, braver at night;
dreaming evil, I have done my hitch
over the plain houses, light by light:
lonely thing, twelve-fingered, out of mind.
A woman like that is not a woman, quite.
I have been her kind.

I have found the warm caves in the woods,
filled them with skillets, carvings, shelves,
closets, silks, innumerable goods;
fixed the suppers for the worms and the elves:
whining, rearranging the disaligned.
A woman like that is misunderstood.
I have been her kind.

I have ridden in your cart, driver,
waved my nude arms at villages going by,
learning the last bright routes, survivor
where your flames still bite my thigh
and my ribs crack where your wheels wind.
A woman like that is not ashamed to die.
I have been her kind.

❦ Oysters

Oysters we ate,
sweet blue babies,
twelve eyes looked up at me,
running with lemon and Tabasco.
I was afraid to eat this father-food
and Father laughed
and drank down his martini,
clear as tears.
It was a soft medicine
that came from the sea into my mouth,
moist and plump.
I swallowed.
It went down like a large pudding.
Then I ate one o'clock and two o'clock.
Then I laughed and then we laughed
and let me take note—
there was a death,
the death of childhood
there at the Union Oyster House
for I was fifteen
and eating oysters
and the child was defeated.
The woman won.

✆ *Planetarium*

(Thinking of Caroline Herschel, 1750–1848,
astronomer, sister of William; and others)

A woman in the shape of a monster
a monster in the shape of a woman
the skies are full of them

a woman   'in the snow
among the Clocks and instruments
or measuring the ground with poles'

in her 98 years to discover
8 comets

she whom the moon ruled
like us
levitating into the night sky
riding the polished lenses

Galaxies of women, there
doing penance for impetuousness
ribs chilled
in those spaces   of the mind

An eye,
        'virile, precise and absolutely certain'
        from the mad webs of Uranisborg
                                encountering the Nova

every impulse of light exploding
from the core
as life flies out of us

    Tycho whispering at last
    'Let me not seem to have lived in vain'

What we see, we see
and seeing is changing

the light that shrivels a mountain
and leaves a man alive

Heartbeat of the pulsar
heart sweating through my body

The radio impulse
pouring in from Taurus

    I am bombarded yet   I stand

I have been standing all my life in the
direct path of a battery of signals
the most accurately transmitted most
untranslateable language in the universe
I am a galactic cloud so deep   so invo-
luted that a light wave could take 15
years to travel through me   And has
taken   I am an instrument in the shape
of a woman trying to translate pulsations
into images   for the relief of the body
and the reconstruction of the mind.

Indonesia
Samiati Alisjahbana (1930–   )

✆ *Quiet Water*

Quiet, only tiny ripples.
A fallen leaf drifts,
Following the wind-driven water.
A dragon-fly slowly settles
On the barely-moving leaf.
Dragon-fly-skipper on a ship of leaf
You sail calmly straight by.

As if the soul were that calm,
Weakly surrendering to this world
Without a protesting motion, not fighting its loneliness,
As if satisfied—and with just this.
And everything will always be just this way,
Only the muddy soil sinking invisibly deeper.

Translated by Burton Raffel and Nurdin Salam

✆ *Childless Woman*

The womb
Rattles its pod, the moon
Discharges itself from the tree with nowhere to go.

My landscape is a hand with no lines,
The roads bunched to a knot,
The knot myself,

Myself the rose you achieve—
This body,
This ivory

Godly as a child's shriek.
Spiderlike, I spin mirrors,
Loyal to my image,

Uttering nothing but blood—
Taste it, dark red!
And my forest

My funeral,
And this hill and this
Gleaming with the mouths of corpses.

America
Linda Pastan (1932–   )

To My Son, Approaching 11

I outgrew childhood once,
served the full sentence
of innocence myself,
grew scales and callouses
to cover all but the
under parts of memory,
a rotting tree trunk
with green vines growing
through its old knot holes
like flowers through the
sockets of a skull.
Stephen, in more than sleep
recurrent dreams come true:
I live it all awake with you.

England
Anne Stevenson (1933–   )

☙ *The Mother*

Of course I love them, they are my children.
That is my daughter and this my son.
And this is my life I give them to please them.
It has never been used. Keep it safe. Pass it on.

Sierra Leone
Femi Sisay (1933–   )

☙ *Yon Pastures Green*

Who knows
What disillusionments await,
What sweetness now will then turn sour
Before the open gate?
Who knows
What tragedies abide
The moment to unfold?
Then, weary traveller plodding on,
Discount not foolishly the present scene
In idle dream of yonder pastures green,
But rather savour well all that there is
That better, sweeter, still may seem
The fruits at journey's end.

ℰ *personal letter no. 2*

i speak skimpily to
you about apartments i
no longer dwell in
and children who
chant their dis
obedience in choruses.
if i were young
i wd stretch you
with my wild words
while our nights
run soft with hands.
but i am what i
am. woman. alone
amid all this noise.

The Practical Clown

My dad was a practical man.

O his big belly is gone.

Father—what's all this?
Poems to sleep on—
A gift from your daughter
To whom you remarked, "You can't
Be sensitive and sensible
At the same time." Why not?

We were angry at each other
For being sensitive and senseless. My father,
It was said,

Wore his heart on his sleeve
Because he was free
Of ambition. Like a woman
He conquered, if at all,
By surrender. When he gave in
To death

I came to life and wrote
This down. Now he lies
In Valhalla shouting,

"Daughter, why are you singing?"

It's awful how the dead can carry on.

ᛯ *The Graffiti Poet*

Who are you?
I grew up in the schoolrooms of the Dakotas,
I sat by the wood stove and longed for spring.
My desk leaned like a clavichord, stripped of its hammers,
and on it I carved my name, forever and ever,
so the seed of that place should never forget me.
Outside, in their beehive tombs, I could hear
the dead spinning extravagant honey.
I remembered their names and wanted only
that the living remember mine.

I am the invisible student, dead end
of a crowded class. I write and nobody answers.
On the Brooklyn Bridge I wrote a poem:
the rain washed it away.
On the walls of the Pentagon I made
my sign: a workman blasted me off like dung.
From the halls of Newark to the shores
of Detroit, I engrave my presence with fire
so the lords of those places may never forget me.

Save me. I can hardly speak. So we pass,
not speaking. In bars where your dreams drink,
I scrawl your name, my name, in a heart
that the morning daily erases.

✆ *The Blackbird*

The wind is a blackbird.
I am a blackbird.
When you watch a blackbird
flying down-wind
you
cannot tell
if the wind is really the wind
or the bird is a bird.

You cannot know
how to listen,
but if you listen
you can tell.

The wind and the blackbird
do not sound
the same.

Canada
Margaret Atwood (1939–   )

ᘓ *More and more*

More and more frequently the edges
of me dissolve and I become
a wish to assimilate the world, including
you, if possible through the skin
like a cool plant's tricks with oxygen
and live by a harmless green burning.

I would not consume
you, or ever
finish, you would still be there
surrounding me, complete
as the air.

Unfortunately I don't have leaves.
Instead I have eyes
and teeth and other non-green
things which rule out osmosis.

So be careful, I mean it,
I give you a fair warning:

This kind of hunger draws
everything into its own
space; nor can we
talk it all over, have a calm
rational discussion.

There is no reason for this, only
a starved dog's logic about bones.

✲ *Legacies*

her grandmother called her from the playground
    "yes, ma'am"
    "i want chu to learn how to make rolls" said the old
woman proudly
but the little girl didn't want
to learn how because she knew
even if she couldn't say it that
that would mean when the old one died she would be less
dependent on her spirit so
she said
    "i don't want to know how to make no rolls"
with her lips poked out
and the old woman wiped her hands on
her apron saying "lord
    these children"
and neither of them ever
said what they meant
and i guess nobody ever does

Nikki Giovanni (1943–   )

ᦆ *Mothers*

the last time i was home
to see my mother we kissed
exchanged pleasantries
and unpleasantries pulled a warm
comforting silence around
us and read separate books

i remember the first time
i consciously saw her
we were living in a three room
apartment on burns avenue

mommy always sat in the dark
i don't know how i knew that but she did

that night i stumbled into the kitchen
maybe because i've always been
a night person or perhaps because i had wet
the bed
she was sitting on a chair
the room was bathed in moonlight diffused through
those thousands of panes landlords who rented
to people with children were prone to put in windows

she may have been smoking but maybe not
her hair was three-quarters her height
which made me a strong believer in the samson myth
and very black

i'm sure i just hung there by the door
i remember thinking: what a beautiful lady

she was very deliberately waiting
perhaps for my father to come home
from his night job or maybe for a dream
that had promised to come by
"come here" she said "i'll teach you
a poem: *i see the moon*
          the moon sees me
          god bless the moon
          and god bless me"
i taught it to my son
who recited it for her
just to say we must learn
to bear the pleasures
as we have borne the pains

✑ *Women*

They were women then
My mama's generation
Husky of voice—Stout of
Step
With fists as well as
Hands
How they battered down
Doors
And ironed
Starched white
Shirts
How they led
Armies
Headragged Generals
Across mined
Fields
Booby-trapped
Ditches
To discover books
Desks
A place for us
How they knew what we
Must know
Without knowing a page
Of it
Themselves.

I shall write of the old men I knew
And the young men
I loved
And of the gold toothed women
Mighty of arm
Who dragged us all
To church.

Puerto Rico
Ángela María Dávila (1944–   )

ᖫ *I Want for My Name . . .*

I want for my name
gray and cutting grave diggers.
Moreover:
I don't want a name,
let the sea take it washing it
in my sand.
Let the ocean drag it,
that I may feel
I am there intact,
without a name.
That I am there, with the vibrations of the blow
of the wave.
With my taste of salt
with my taste of foam,
shaking with the taste of the green sea.
Alone with my skin and with my valleys,
with my eyes inside, my river basins,
with my ardent shores,
gathered in flocks of murmurs
nameless.
The throbbing ocean is alone,
pulsating love of waves and lullabies . . .

Translated by María Arrillaga

America
Anne Waldman (1945–   )

⟨♦⟩ *Mother Country*

What is around me is
this huge shape I can't visualize
from here, sitting here quietly
nights go by the same way
noisy people outside on the block
I want to move from
so I can understand it better

Not all streets are like this one
bursting with so much energy
you can't keep still
with cops watching over every second
nothing gets out of hand out there
but does deep inside you somewhere
down in your American soul

It's hard to kill, harder still to love
where you come from when it hurts you
but you know you do, you do

Indonesia
Siti Nuraini (c. 1960)

✆ *A Woman*

A woman who languidly breaks
a dry twig, leaning out of the high
rectangular window; a distant secret
calls, an odd sensation touches her heart.

Her soul is occupied, a lake lies open,
a second world at the border of her being.
Love and longing roll
in the deeps, never once coming to the surface.

Her bleak house, embraced by solitude,
chases away the birds into the night.
She herself shivers, hesitates
at the threshold, panics, then in time
jerks the door open, and her face falls closed.

Translated by James S. Holmes

Martinique
Marie-Thérèse Rouil (c. 1970s)

↶ Childhood

I'm the little black child,
With eyes as big as my face,
My face as smooth as a mango,
A mango . . . there's something I know!

They say my hair is curled up tight,
Curled as tight as wool.
Wool? Don't know what that is!

But I live naked and free,
As free as a pigeon!
A pigeon . . . there's something I know!

They tell me my voice is pure,
As pure as crystal.
Crystal? Don't know what that is!

But my body is good and straight,
Good and straight as a palm-tree!
A palm-tree . . . there's something I know!

They tell me my laughter bubbles,
Bubbles like champagne.
Champagne? Don't know what that is!

But I dance, I dance
To the tom-tom's beat!
The tom-tom . . . there's something I know!

Translated by Norman R. Shapiro

ℭ *Simple-song*

When we are going toward someone we say
you are just like me
your thoughts are my brothers
word matches word
how easy to be together.

When we are leaving someone we say
how strange you are
we cannot communicate
we can never agree
how hard, hard and weary to be together.

We are not different nor alike
but each strange in his leather body
sealed in skin and reaching out clumsy hands
and loving is an act
that cannot outlive
the open hand
the open eye
the door in the chest standing open.

✷ *Portrait*

mama spent pennies
in uh gallon milk jug
saved pennies
fuh four babies
college educashun

and when the babies
got bigger they would
secretly "borrow" mama's
pennies to buy candy

and pop cause mama
saved extras
fuh college educashuns
and pop and candy

was uh non-credit in bad teeth
mama pooled pennies
in uh gallon milk jug,
Borden's by the way

and the babies went
to school cause mama saved
and spent and paid
fuh four babies

college educashuns
mama spent pennies
              and nickels
              and quarters
              and dollars

and one life.
mama spent her life
in uh gallon milk jug
fuh four black babies
college educashuns.

✆ *Confession to Settle a Curse*

You don't
know
who I am
because
you don't know
my mother
she's always been an exemplary mother
told me so herself
there were reasons she
had to lock
everything that could be locked
there's much can be
locked
in a good German household crowded
with wardrobes dressers sideboards
bookcases cupboards chests bureaus
desks trunks caskets coffers all with lock
and key
and locked
it was lots of trouble
for her
just carry that enormous key ring
be bothered all the time

I wanted scissors stationery
my winter coat and she had to unlock
the drawer get it out and lock
all up again
me she reproached for lacking
confidence not being open
I have a mother I can tell everything
she told me so
I've
been bound
made fast
locked
by the key witch
but a small
winner
I'm not
in turn locking
a child
in my arms

✆ *The Palm-Reading*

When I was once familiar
with the family faces,
they told us our own stories
before we had the chance;
My brother was to control
arithmetic, and from me
they expected nothing much.
I felt followed by a wasp,
buzzing the repetition
of my story into my head.

After my brother's second attempt
to burn down the house,
a misreading was announced.
Though too late to make any change
we tried family picnics
at the penny arcade. I walked behind
with my own nickels. I tried
to refuse the women and boys who lived
off our acceptances;
I loved their quiet proposals.

Now, the love music we sang
seems like the recital
of a dead person's journal.
I am bored with my normalcy;
It's hard to keep awake.
I want to go where my life is,
without the stories I tell.
Though it may move
like a walk into the sea,
it goes darkly and cool.
I know it is alive.

Index